ACHIEVE LEVEL 6

ENGLISH
Practice Questions

Maddy Barnes

RISING STARS

Rising Stars UK Ltd, 7 Hatchers Mews, Bermondsey Street, London SE1 3GS

www.risingstars-uk.com

Every effort has been made to trace copyright holders and obtain their permission for the use of copyright materials. The publishers will gladly receive information enabling them to rectify any error or omission in subsequent editions.

All facts are correct at time of going to press.

First published 2013
Reprinted with revisions 2013
This edition incorporating revisions 2014
Text, design and layout © Rising Stars UK Ltd 2014

Project manager: Dawn Booth
Editorial: Marieke O'Connor
Proofreader: Claire Shewbridge
Design: Words & Pictures Ltd, London
Cover design: Marc Burville-Riley

Acknowledgements:
p.6 *Spilled Water*, Sally Grindley, published by Bloomsbury; p.8 *100 Shades of White*, Preethi Nair, published by HarperCollins; p.8 *A Suitable Boy*, Vikram Seth, published by David Goodwin Associates; p.10 *Macavity: the Mystery Cat*, published by Faber & Faber; p.12 *The Great Blue Yonder*, Alex Shearer, published by Macmillan Children's Books; p.14 *Heartland*, Lauren Brooke, published by Scholastic; p.16 *Cosmic*, Frank Cottrell Boyle, published by Macmillan Children's Books; p.18 'F.E.A.R.', Ian Brown, Dave McCracken and Dave Colquhoun, Universal; p.20 *This Room*, Imtiaz Dharker, published by Bloodaxe Books; p.22 *Toast*, Nigel Slater, published by HarperCollins; p.24 *Bootleg*, Alex Shearer, published by Macmillan Children's Books; p.26 *Boo!*, Kevin Crossley-Holland, published by Oxford University Press; p.28 *Mr Ifonly*, Brian Patten, published by Macmillan Children's Books; p.30 *The Song of a Battery Hen*, Edwin Brock, published by Secker & Warburg; p.32 *Creator of Unity*, Levi Tafari; p.34 *A Suitable Boy*, Vikram Seth, published by David Goodwin Associates

British Library Cataloguing-in-Publication Data
A CIP record for this book is available from the British Library.

ISBN: 978-1-78339-420-3
Printed in India by Multivista Global Ltd

Contents

How to use this book

What we have included:

1 This book gives you a set of warm-up practice questions, organised by topic. These questions will provide practice in all the Level 5 tricky bits included in the Achieve Level 6 English Revision book.

2 Each question has lines to write your answers and a specific number of marks (like a real National Test question). Answers are included in the middle of the book.

3 Marking guidance is provided.

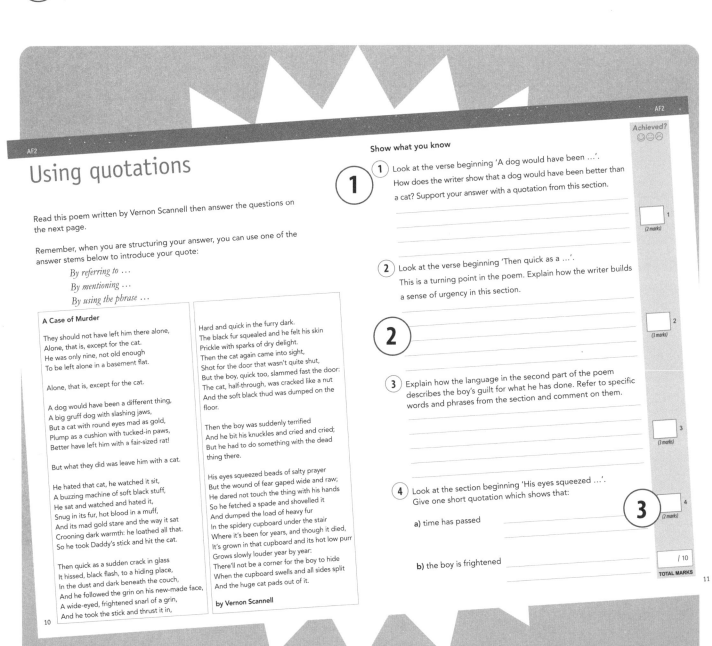

Topic questions

(1) There are sets of questions on all the topics you need to cover for the English National Tests, many of which are based on extracts from books and poems. Most topics include some questions on using and applying your knowledge of English.

(2) Each topic matches a section in the Achieve Level 6 English Revision book.

(3) Each question has lines for you to write your answers and a specific number of marks (like a real National Test question). Answers are included in the middle of the book.

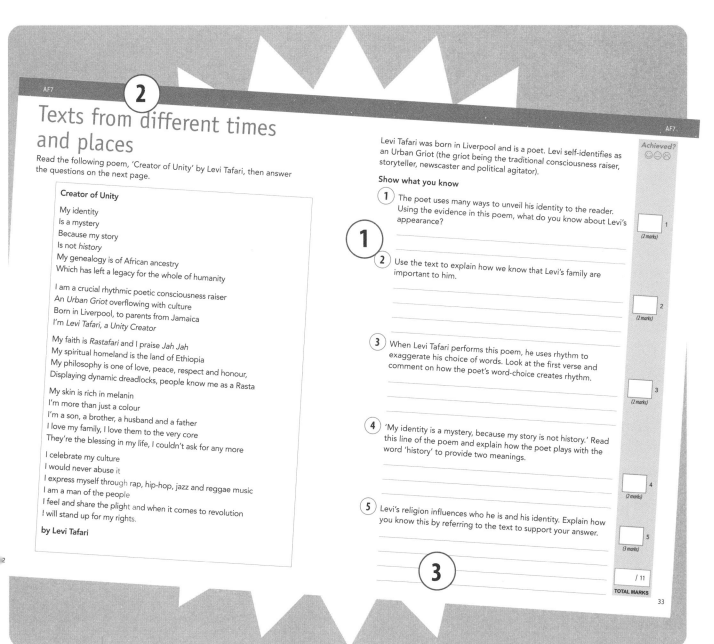

AF7

Texts from different times and places

Read the following poem, 'Creator of Unity' by Levi Tafari, then answer the questions on the next page.

Creator of Unity

My identity
Is a mystery
Because my story
Is not *history*
My genealogy is of African ancestry
Which has left a legacy for the whole of humanity

I am a crucial rhythmic poetic consciousness raiser
An *Urban Griot* overflowing with culture
Born in Liverpool, to parents from Jamaica
I'm *Levi Tafari*, a Unity Creator

My faith is *Rastafari* and I praise *Jah Jah*
My spiritual homeland is the land of Ethiopia
My philosophy is one of love, peace, respect and honour,
Displaying dynamic dreadlocks, people know me as a Rasta

My skin is rich in melanin
I'm more than just a colour
I'm a son, a brother, a husband and a father
I love my family, I love them to the very core
They're the blessing in my life, I couldn't ask for any more

I celebrate my culture
I would never abuse it
I express myself through rap, hip-hop, jazz and reggae music
I am a man of the people
I feel and share the plight and when it comes to revolution
I will stand up for my rights.

by Levi Tafari

Levi Tafari was born in Liverpool and is a poet. Levi self-identifies as an Urban Griot (the griot being the traditional consciousness raiser, storyteller, newscaster and political agitator).

Achieved?

Show what you know

(1) The poet uses many ways to unveil his identity to the reader. Using the evidence in this poem, what do you know about Levi's appearance?

_____ 1

(2 marks)

(2) Use the text to explain how we know that Levi's family are important to him.

_____ 2

(2 marks)

(3) When Levi Tafari performs this poem, he uses rhythm to exaggerate his choice of words. Look at the first verse and comment on how the poet's word-choice creates rhythm.

_____ 3

(2 marks)

(4) 'My identity is a mystery, because my story is not history.' Read this line of the poem and explain how the poet plays with the word 'history' to provide two meanings.

_____ 4

(2 marks)

(5) Levi's religion influences who he is and his identity. Explain how you know this by referring to the text to support your answer.

_____ 5

(3 marks)

/ 11

TOTAL MARKS

33

Identifying points in a text

An example of ...

It means that ...

It refers to ...

Read this extract from *Spilled Water* by Sally Grindley, then answer the questions on identifying points in a text on the next page.

Spilled Water

We never had much money, but I didn't really notice because neither did anyone else in our village. Father's favourite saying was, 'If you realise that you have enough, you are truly rich,' and he believed it. 'We have fresh food and warm clothes, a roof over our heads (a bit leaky when it rains) and a wooden bed to sleep on. What more can we ask for?' he demanded. 'And not only that,' he continued, 'but I have the finest little dumpling of a daughter in the whole of China.'

My parents worked hard to make sure that we always had enough. Father set off early in the morning, his farming tools over his shoulder, to tend the dozens of tiny terraces of vegetables that straggled higgledy-piggledy over the hillside above and below our house. He dug and sowed and weeded and cropped throughout the numbing cold of winter and the suffocating heat of summer. In the middle of the day, he returned home clutching triumphantly a gigantic sheaf of pakchoi, a basin of bright greens, or a bucket full of melon-sized turnips.

'Your father can grow the biggest, tastiest vegetables on a piece of land the size of a silk handkerchief,' Mother used to say, and I would skip off to help him because I wanted one day to grow the biggest, tastiest vegetables as well.

by Sally Grindley

Show what you know

1 Find and copy a word which shows how the father feels when he brings the vegetables home for his family.

_____

1

(1 mark)

2 Life is not easy for the girl and her family. Using the text, explain how you know this.

_____

_____

2

_____

(3 marks)

_____

3 '"Your father can grow the biggest, tastiest vegetables on a piece of land the size of a silk handkerchief," Mother used to say.' What does this tell you about the mother's opinion of the father?

_____

_____

3

_____

(3 marks)

_____

4 '... tiny terraces of vegetables that straggled higgledy-piggledy over the hillside...' What does this tell you about the area?

_____

_____

4

(2 marks)

_____

5 There is no interaction between the characters in this extract; however, it is obvious that the child respects her father. Find some evidence to support this view.

_____

_____

5

_____

(2 marks)

6 Although the father does not say he loves his daughter, the author gives us the impression that he does. Find and copy a phrase which illustrates this.

6

(1 mark)

/ 12

TOTAL MARKS

_____

7

Using information from different sources

Here are two descriptions of India from two different sources. Both are examples of subjective writing. Read them both and then answer the questions on the next page.

Extract 1

100 Shades of White

The driver pulled up to the Taj, a five-star hotel in the middle of the city. The floors were made of white marble and the ceilings were high, beautifully sculptured with intricate designs and painted in fresh, clean white. Hanging from them were ornate crystal chandeliers. The air conditioning was switched on so you wouldn't have to open the windows because when you did, the opulence of where you were living made you feel guilty. The same contradiction that resided in this place resided in me. The same India, where I was from, gave birth to a mass of antitheses; happiness, sadness, poverty, richness, abundance, hunger, piety, decadence which engulfed its people. All co-existing together.

by Preethi Nair

Extract 2

A Suitable Boy

Between the inner entrance and the river was the celebrated garden and the small but exquisite palace. The garden itself was a triumph as much of geometry as of horticulture. It was unlikely in fact that the flowers with which it was now planted – other than jasmine and the dark red, deep-scented Indian rose – were the same as those for which it had been planned more than two centuries ago. What few flowers remained now looked exhausted from the daily heat. But the well-tended, well-watered lawns, the great, shady neem trees dispersed symmetrically about the grounds, and the narrow sandstone strips that divided the flower-beds and lawns into octagons and squares provided an island of calm in a troubled and crowded town.

by Vikram Seth

Show what you know

(**1**) Using Extract 1, give your opinion of India.

_____

_____

_____

_____

| | 1 |

(2 marks)

(**2**) Using Extract 2, give your opinion of India.

_____

_____

_____

_____

| | 2 |

(2 marks)

(**3**) In Extract 1, the author refers to feeling guilty. Explain why you think this is so.

_____

_____

_____

_____

_____

| | 3 |

(2 marks)

(**4**) Extract 2 focuses more on a physical description of India. What effect does this have on the reader?

_____

_____

_____

_____

| | 4 |

(2 marks)

(**5**) Both extracts provide vivid descriptions of India. Which extract do you prefer and why? Use the text to support your answer.

_____

_____

_____

_____

| | 5 |

(2 marks)

| | / 10 |

TOTAL MARKS

Using quotations

Read this poem by T.S. Eliot, and then answer the questions on the next page.

Remember, when you are structuring your answer, you can use one of the answer stems below to introduce your quote:

By referring to …

By mentioning …

By using the phrase …

Macavity: the Mystery Cat

Macavity's a Mystery Cat: he's called the Hidden Paw—
For he's the master criminal who can defy the Law.
He's the bafflement of Scotland Yard, the Flying Squad's despair:
For when they reach the scene of crime—Macavity's not there!

Macavity, Macavity, there's no one like Macavity,
He's broken every human law, he breaks the law of gravity.
His powers of levitation would make a fakir stare,
And when you reach the scene of crime—Macavity's not there!
You may seek him in the basement, you may look up in the air—
But I tell you once and once again, Macavity's not there!

Macavity's a ginger cat, he's very tall and thin;
You would know him if you saw him, for his eyes are sunken in.
His brow is deeply lined with thought, his head is highly domed;
His coat is dusty from neglect, his whiskers are uncombed.
He sways his head from side to side, with movements like a snake;
And when you think he's half asleep, he's always wide awake.

Macavity, Macavity, there's no one like Macavity,
For he's a fiend in feline shape, a monster of depravity.
You may meet him in a by-street, you may see him in the square—
But when a crime's discovered, then Macavity's not there!

He's outwardly respectable. (They say he cheats at cards.)
And his footprints are not found in any file of Scotland Yard's
And when the larder's looted, or the jewel-case is rifled,
Or when the milk is missing, or another Peke's been stifled,
Or the greenhouse glass is broken, and the trellis past repair—
Ay, there's the wonder of the thing! Macavity's not there!

And when the Foreign Office find a Treaty's gone astray,
Or the Admiralty lose some plans and drawings by the way,
There may be a scrap of paper in the hall or on the stair—
But it's useless to investigate—Macavity's not there!
And when the loss has been disclosed, the Secret Service say:
'It must have been Macavity!'—but he's a mile away.
You'll be sure to find him resting, or a-licking of his thumbs;
Or engaged in doing complicated long division sums.

Macavity, Macavity, there's no one like Macavity,
There never was a cat of such deceitfulness and suavity.
He always has an alibi, and one or two to spare:
At whatever time the deed took place—MACAVITY WASN'T THERE!
And they say that all the Cats whose wicked deeds are widely known
(I might mention Mungojerrie, I might mention Griddlebone)
Are nothing more than agents for the Cat who all the time
Just controls their operations: the Napoleon of Crime!

by T.S. Eliot

Show what you know

1 Read the third verse, beginning 'Macavity's a ginger cat ...', in which the poet describes Macavity's appearance. Give one short quotation which suggests that:

a) Macavity is intelligent

_____

_____

	1

(2 marks)

b) Macavity is not well looked-after

_____

_____

2 What do Macavity's actions throughout the poem reveal about his personality and abilities? Explain as fully as you can, using quotations from the text to support your answer.

_____

_____

_____

_____

	2

(3 marks)

_____

3 Quote a line from the poem that contains the following forms of figurative language:

a) simile

_____

_____

	3

(2 marks)

b) allusion

_____

_____

4 How does the poet create humour in the poem? Explain as fully as you can, using quotations from the text to support your answer.

_____

	4

(3 marks)

_____

_____

_____

/ 10

TOTAL MARKS

Different meanings

Read this extract from *The Great Blue Yonder* by Alex Shearer, then answer the questions on the next page.

The Great Blue Yonder

People seem to think it's an easy life when you're dead. But you can take it from me, it's no such thing.

For a start, grown-ups keep coming up to you and saying, 'Oi, you! You're young to be on your own, aren't you? Are you looking for your mum?'

And when you say, 'No. She's still alive, I died before she did,' they say, 'Tut-tut, that's not so good then,' as if there was something you could do about it to change everything, and that it was your fault you weren't still breathing.

In fact they seem to think that you've even gone and pushed in or something, and pinched someone else's place in the queue.

The way people seem to see it here 'over on the other side' as Arthur likes to call it (I'll tell you about Arthur in a minute) is that everything's done according to age and experience – just like at home.

I call it 'home' anyway. Arthur calls it 'the side'. He says that being alive must be 'the side' or else being dead couldn't be on the 'other side'. Well, that's what he says, though it doesn't make much sense to me.

How it seems to work is that you're supposed to have a good long life, and then when you get to be really old, you just sort of fade away and die of nothing in particular. And Arthur says that the best way to do it is to die in bed with your boots on. But I can't quite see what you'd be doing in bed with your boots on – unless you were too ill to take them off. But even then, you'd think that someone would take them off for you. And all I know is that if I'd ever gone to bed with my boots on, my mum would have had fifty fits. Sixty fits, maybe. Probably even a hundred fits.

by Alex Shearer

Show what you know

1 'People seem to think it's an easy life when you're dead. But you can take it from me, it's no such thing.' What can you infer about the main character from this text?

_____

_____

_____

_____

| | 1 |

(2 marks)

2 Using the text to support your answer, how is being dead conveyed here?

_____

_____

_____

_____

| | 2 |

(2 marks)

3 The main character and Arthur do not agree on everything – explain how we know this.

_____

_____

_____

_____

| | 3 |

(2 marks)

4 Find some evidence in this extract which suggests that the main character is not scared of being dead.

_____

_____

_____

_____

| | 4 |

(3 marks)

5 '… as if there was something you could do about it to change everything, and that it was your fault you weren't still breathing.' How is this line an effective way of conveying the character's opinion?

_____

_____

_____

_____

| | 5 |

(2 marks)

| / 11 |

TOTAL MARKS

The wider importance of ideas

Read this extract from *Heartland* by Lauren Brooke, then answer the questions on the next page.

Heartland

'Easy now,' Amy Fleming murmured to Melody as the mare pulled against the long-line and whickered restlessly to her foal. Daybreak, the four-day-old filly, trotted inquisitively around the field, heedless of Melody's concern, her arched neck and intelligent head held high, her tiny hooves flicking lightly over the snow-covered grass. The pale November sun shone down on her bright chestnut coat. *The perfect Thanksgiving day …*

Amy held back her thoughts. No, she didn't want to think about it being Thanksgiving. That's why she was out here with Melody and Daybreak instead of being in the farmhouse with Grandpa and her older sister, Lou. That's why she'd been working non-stop on the yard all day. She didn't want to think about it being her first Thanksgiving without Mom.

Melody whinnied again.

'It's OK, girl,' Amy said, her fingers moving in light circles on Melody's neck. 'Your baby's safe. She's just taking a look around.'

Registering the familiar, comforting touch of Amy's hands, Melody turned her head. Amy rubbed the mare's forehead and felt her relax slightly. *If you're here*, Melody seemed to be saying, *then everything must be OK.*

A warm glow spread through Amy as she saw the trust in the mare's eyes. Only a month ago, it had all been so different. When Melody had first arrived at Heartland, the horse sanctuary founded by Amy's late mother, she had been exceptionally wary. But gradually she came to trust Amy and, after Amy had assisted at Daybreak's birth, the bond between them seemed to deepen further.

by Lauren Brooke

Show what you know

1 How can you tell that Daybreak is a confident foal?

_____

_____

2 Why is Amy avoiding the Thanksgiving celebrations?

_____

_____

3 Using the text to support your answer, explain what Amy's relationship with Melody is like now.

_____

_____

_____

_____

4 At the end of this extract, the author thinks back to a month ago – this provides the reader with more information about the relationship between Amy and Melody. Using the text to support you, how has their relationship changed?

_____

_____

_____

_____

5 Amy needs the horses as much as they need her. Explain in your own words how Amy needs them.

_____

_____

_____

6 There are two examples where the author has used italics in this extract. Write down one example and explain why it is in italics.

_____

_____

_____

_____

Achieved?
☺ ☺ ☹

| | 1 |
(1 mark)

| | 2 |
(1 mark)

| | 3 |
(2 marks)

| | 4 |
(3 marks)

| | 5 |
(2 marks)

| | 6 |
(2 marks)

| / 11 |

TOTAL MARKS

Organisation of the text

Read this extract from *Cosmic* by Frank Cottrell Boyce, then answer the questions on the next page.

Cosmic

Mum, Dad – if you're listening – you know I said I was going to the South Lakeland Outdoor Activity Centre with the school? To be completely honest, I'm not exactly in the Lake District.

To be completely honest, I'm more sort of in space.

I'm on this rocket, the Infinite Possibility. I'm about two thousand miles above the surface of the Earth. I'm all right … ish.

I know I've got some explaining to do. This is me doing it.

I lied about my age. I sort of gave the impression I was about thirty. Obviously I'm more sort of thirteen-ish. On my next birthday.

To be fair, everyone lies about their age. Adults pretend to be younger. Teenagers pretend to be older. Children wish they were grown-ups. Grown-ups wish they were children.

It's not like I had to try very hard, is it? Everyone thinks I'm older than I really am, just because I'm tall. In St Joan of Arc Primary the teachers seemed to think that height and age were the same thing. If you were taller than someone, you must be older than them. If you were tall and you made a mistake – even if it was only your first day – you got, 'You should know better, big lad like you.'

Why, by the way? Why should a big lad know better just because he's big? King Kong's a big lad. Would he know the way to the toilet block on his first day at school? When no one had told him? No, I don't think he would.

by Frank Cottrell Boyce

Show what you know

(1) How does the author engage with the reader in the opening sentences?

_____

_____

☐ 1

(2 marks)

(2) Why do you think the author repeats 'To be completely honest …'?

_____

_____

_____

_____

☐ 2

(2 marks)

(3) Find and copy some evidence which shows that the author thinks it is okay to tell a lie.

_____

_____

_____

_____

☐ 3

(1 mark)

(4) This is the opening chapter to a book which was shortlisted for the Guardian Children's Fiction Prize and the Roald Dahl Funny Prize, and a reviewer in the *Mail on Sunday* wrote: 'five-laughs-a-page, fall-off-the-chair funny'. Explain how the author uses comedy. Refer to the text in your answer.

_____

_____

_____

_____

☐ 4

(2 marks)

(5) Read the closing paragraph. What is the purpose of the repeated use of questions?

_____

_____

_____

_____

☐ 5

(2 marks)

/ 9

TOTAL MARKS

17

Themes and purposes

Read the following song, F.E.A.R., written by Ian Brown, Dave McCracken and Dave Colquhoun, then answer the questions on the next page.

F.E.A.R.

For each a road

For everyman a religion

Find everybody and rule

Everything and rumble

Forget everything and remember

For everything a reason

Forgive everybody and remember

For each a road

For everyman a religion

Face everybody and rule

Everything and rumble

Forget everything and remember

For everything a reason

You got the fear

You got the fear

You got the fear

You got the fear

F.E.A.R.

Finding eternity arouses reactions

Freeing excellence affects reality

Fallen empires are running

Find earth and reap

Fantastic expectations

Amazing revelations

Final execution and resurrection

Free expression as revolution

Finding everything and realizing

by Ian Brown, Dave McCracken and Dave Colquhoun

Show what you know

(1) This song is called F.E.A.R. and, in most cases, the lines are an acrostic of the word 'fear', e.g.

For **e**ach **a** **r**oad
For **e**verything **a** **r**eason

Comment on how effective this is for organising song lyrics.

_____

_____

_____

_____

1

(3 marks)

(2) Explain what you think the main theme of this song is, using the lyrics to support your answer.

_____

_____

_____

_____

2

(3 marks)

(3) In an interview with _Clash_ magazine, when asked what his inspiration for F.E.A.R. was, Ian Brown answered that _The Autobiography of Malcolm X_ (which preached the study of etymology so that one could have 'control over people through the use of language') had influenced him to create the many acronyms for FEAR. Choose a three-lettered word of your own and create three acronyms for it.

Word: _____

_____

_____

_____

_____

3

(3 marks)

(4) This song has been written in a unique way. Explain the more conventional features that song lyrics usually have.

_____

_____

_____

_____

4

(3 marks)

/ 12

TOTAL MARKS

19

Explaining how language is used

Read the poem, 'This Room', by Imtiaz Dharker, then answer the questions on the next page.

This Room

This room is breaking out
of itself, cracking through
its own walls
in search of space, light,
empty air.

The bed is lifting out of
its nightmares.
From dark corners, chairs
are rising up to crash through clouds.

This is the time and place
to be alive:
when the daily furniture of our lives
stirs, when the improbable arrives.
Pots and pans bang together
in celebration, clang
past the crowd of garlic, onions, spices,
fly by the ceiling fan.
No one is looking for the door.

In all this excitement
I'm wondering where
I've left my feet, and why

my hands are outside, clapping.

by Imtiaz Dharker

Show what you know

1 Find an example of personification in the opening lines of the poem.

_____

_____

1
(1 mark)

2 Find an example of where rhyme is used in this poem.

_____

_____

2
(1 mark)

3 This poem is made up of an extended metaphor which symbolises the poet moving on from or breaking free from something. Throughout the poem the author uses words and images which have an element of movement and onomatopoeia – find an example.

_____

_____

3
(1 mark)

4 How does the mood change throughout the poem? Use the text to support your answer.

_____

_____

_____

4
(2 marks)

5 This is a very happy poem. How does Imtiaz Dharker suggest her joy in it?

_____

_____

_____

5
(3 marks)

6 We do not know the cause of the joyful explosion in the poem. List some ideas which could change your own mood to one of happiness and fulfilment.

_____

_____

_____

6
(2 marks)

/ 10

TOTAL MARKS

Language choice and effectiveness

Read the extract from *Toast* by Nigel Slater, then answer the questions on the next page.

Toast
Arctic Roll

There were only three of us at school whose house wasn't joined to the one next door. Number 67 Sandringham Road, always referred to as 'York House', had mock-Tudor wooden beams, a double garage of which one half doubled as a garden shed and repository for my brothers' canoes, and a large and crumbling greenhouse. I was the only one ever to have tasted Arctic Roll. While my friends made do with the pink, white and brown stripes of a Neapolitan ice-cream brick, my father would bring out this newfangled frozen gourmet dessert. Arctic Roll was a sponge-covered tube of vanilla ice-cream, its USP being the wrapping of wet sponge and ring of red jam so thin it could have been drawn on with an architect's pen.

As treats go, this was the big one, bigger even than a Cadbury's MiniRoll. This wasn't a holiday or celebration treat like trifle. This was a treat with no obvious occasion. Its appearance had nothing to do with being good, having done well in a school test, having been kind or thoughtful. It was just a treat, served with as much pomp as if it were a roasted swan at a Tudor banquet. I think it was a subtle reminder to the assembled family and friends of how well my father's business was doing. Whatever, there was no food that achieved such an ovation in our house. Quite an achievement for something I always thought tasted like frozen carpet.

by Nigel Slater

Show what you know

1 Read the description of an Arctic Roll in the first paragraph. How does the author use sarcasm to demonstrate his point?

_____

_____

_____

1

(2 marks)

2 Referring to the text, explain how the author effectively describes how much of a treat an Arctic Roll really was.

_____

_____

_____

_____

2

(3 marks)

3 'Quite an achievement for something I always thought tasted like frozen carpet.' As a summary to this extract, the writer's choice of language here is humorous. Explain why.

_____

_____

_____

_____

_____

3

(3 marks)

4 This extract is taken from Nigel Slater's award-winning autobiography. Explain how the author's use of language matched the purpose. Refer to specific words and phrases from the extract.

_____

_____

_____

_____

_____

4

(2 marks)

/ 10

TOTAL MARKS

The effect of sentence structure

Read the following extract from *Bootleg* by Alex Shearer, then answer the questions on the next page.

Bootleg

After a few minutes, the man closed the bonnet of his van and sauntered over to where the boys were playing.

'Having a kickabout, lads?' he asked.

'That's it,' Smudger said. It was pretty obvious what they were doing.

'Hungry work kicking a ball about,' the man continued. 'Makes you a mite peckish, as I remember from my footballing days.'

Huntly and Smudger exchanged a look. They stopped kicking the bottle.

'Yes,' the man went on, 'very hungry work is kicking a ball – even a bottle – about. Makes you long for some kind of high-energy food supplement. Something full of energy to give you a bit of a *Boost!* Something with a bit of *Fruit and Nut* in it. Makes you wonder how they cope in the rest of the *Galaxy*. Makes you wonder if they play football on *Mars*. I sometimes wonder if there's life up there in the *Milky Way*. But you'd have to be quite a *Smartie* pants to know the answer to that one.'

And having delivered this odd speech, the man returned to his van and stood up by the back door, leaning on the roof, and staring up at the sky.

Huntly and Smudger looked questioningly at each other.

Was this him? The black marketer? He certainly didn't look like one. Not for a moment. He seemed quite ordinary. You'd never have thought …

But yes! That was the whole idea. You'd never have suspected for a moment.

by Alex Shearer

Show what you know

1 What does the verb 'sauntered' tell us about how the man walked over to the boys?

_____

_____

| 1 |
(1 mark)

2 'Huntly and Smudger exchanged a look.' Find another example in the text which means almost the same as this quotation.

_____

_____

| 2 |
(1 mark)

3 This extract is taken from a book called *Bootleg*, where *The Good For You Party* is in power and has banned all food with sugar – including chocolate! Smudger and Huntly are determined to find a bootlegger or black marketer to sell them chocolate. Read the paragraph beginning '"Yes", the man went on' and explain how effective the bootlegger's speech is, due to the author's word choice. Refer to the text in your answer.

_____

_____

_____

_____

| 3 |
(3 marks)

4 'And having delivered this odd speech, the man returned to his van and stood up by the back door, leaning on the roof, and staring up at the sky.' What do you think is the purpose of this long sentence in this extract?

_____

_____

_____

_____

| 4 |
(2 marks)

5 Comment on the function of questions and exclamation in the closing five lines of this extract.

_____

_____

_____

_____

| 5 |
(3 marks)

| / 10 |

TOTAL MARKS

Writers' techniques

Read the extract from a short story called 'Boo!' by Kevin Crossley-Holland, then answer the following questions.

Boo!

She didn't like it at all when her father had to go down to London and, for the first time, she had to sleep alone in the old house.

She went up to her bedroom early. She turned the key and locked the door. She latched the windows and drew the curtains. She peered inside her wardrobe, and pulled open the bottom drawer of her chest-of-drawers; she got down on her knees and looked under the bed.

She undressed; she put on her nightdress.

She pulled back the heavy linen cover and climbed into bed. Not to read but to try and sleep – she wanted to sleep as soon as she could. She reached out and turned off the lamp.

'That's good,' said a little voice. 'Now we're safely locked in for the night.'

by Kevin Crossley-Holland

Show what you know

1 Referring to the first two paragraphs only, how do you know that the girl was feeling nervous and anxious?

_____

_____

_____

2 What is the effect of starting almost every sentence with the word 'She'?

_____

_____

_____

_____

_____

2

(2 marks)

3 The author has used a range of compound sentences which follow the structure of:

She _____ and _____.

What atmosphere does this create?

_____

_____

_____

_____

_____

3

(2 marks)

4 'She undressed; she put on her nightdress.' Why do you think the author chose to present this sentence by itself?

_____

_____

_____

_____

_____

4

(2 marks)

5 How does the author create surprise and tension at the end of this short story?

_____

_____

_____

_____

_____

_____

5

(3 marks)

/ 11

TOTAL MARKS

Understanding and commenting on a writer's viewpoint

Read the following poem, 'Mr Ifonly', by Brian Patten, then answer the following questions.

Mr Ifonly

Mr Ifonly sat down and he sighed,
I could have done more if only I had tried

If only I had followed my true intent
If only I had done the things that I meant

If only I had done the things that I could
And not simply done the things that I should

If only a day had lasted a year
And I had not lived in constant fear

Mr Ifonly sat down and he cried:
I could *really* have lived if only I had tried!

Now life has passed me by and it's such a crime,
Said Mr Ifonly who had run out of time.

by Brian Patten

Show what you know

(1) Brian Patten has created a character for this poem – why do you think he called him Mr Ifonly?

_____

_____

_____

1

(3 marks)

Achieved?

☺ 😐 ☹

2 How does the writer show that he empathises and sympathises with Mr Ifonly? Use quotations from the poem to support your answer.

_____

_____

_____

_____

| 2 |

(3 marks)

3 'If only I had done the things that I could / And not simply done the things that I should.' What might the author / Mr Ifonly be referring to here? Give an example from the text about what he could do and what he should do.

_____

_____

_____

_____

_____

| 3 |

(2 marks)

4 Choose two lines from this poem which you find effective and explain why.

_____

_____

_____

_____

| 4 |

(2 marks)

5 How does the poet try to explain the consequences of regret to the reader? Use the text to support your answer.

_____

_____

_____

_____

| 5 |

(3 marks)

| / 13 |

TOTAL MARKS

Creating effects

Read this extract from a poem called 'The Song of a Battery Hen' by Edwin Brock, then answer the questions below.

The Song of a Battery Hen

Listen. Outside this house there's an
Orchard with small moss-green apple
Trees; beyond that, two fields of
Cabbages: then, on the far side of
The road, a broiler house. Listen;
One cockerel crows out of there, as
Tall and proud as the first hour of the sun.
Sometimes I stop calling with the others
To listen, and I wonder if he hears me.
The next time you come here, look for me.
Notice the way I sound inside my head.
God made us all quite differently,
And blessed us with this expensive home.

Edwin Brock

Show what you know

1 Through precise language choices, Edwin Brock transports the reader into the mind of a battery hen. Using the text to support you, explain how the hen reflects on life outside of the battery farm.

_____

_____

_____

_____

2 What effect does writing in the first person have on the reader?

_____

_____

_____

Language and the effect of time

Language is constantly evolving, which means that word meanings can change over time and some words have become obsolete (fallen out of use or been replaced by new words). This also means that new words are added to the *Oxford English Dictionary*. Here are some of the most recent additions – use a dictionary to find out what they mean and write in each one's definition to complete the table.

(16 marks)

Word	Definition
1 muggle	
2 threequel	
3 blamestorming	
4 screenager	
5 lookism	
6 bouncebackability	
7 bling	
8 twitterati	
9 whovian	
10 chillax	
11 unfriend	
12 mini-me	
13 cyberslacking	
14 ego-surfing	
15 meatspace	
16 locavore	

/ 16

TOTAL MARKS

Texts from different times and places

Read the following poem, 'Creator of Unity' by Levi Tafari, then answer the questions on the next page.

Creator of Unity

My identity
Is a mystery
Because my story
Is not *history*
My genealogy is of African ancestry
Which has left a legacy for the whole of humanity

I am a crucial rhythmic poetic consciousness raiser
An *Urban Griot* overflowing with culture
Born in Liverpool, to parents from Jamaica
I'm *Levi Tafari,* a *Unity Creator*

My faith is *Rastafari* and I praise *Jah Jah*
My spiritual homeland is the land of Ethiopia
My philosophy is one of love, peace, respect and honour,
Displaying dynamic dreadlocks, people know me as a Rasta

My skin is rich in melanin
I'm more than just a colour
I'm a son, a brother, a husband and a father
I love my family, I love them to the very core
They're the blessing in my life, I couldn't ask for any more

I celebrate my culture
I would never abuse it
I express myself through rap, hip-hop, jazz and reggae music
I am a man of the people
I feel and share the plight and when it comes to revolution
I will stand up for my rights.

by Levi Tafari

Levi Tafari was born in Liverpool and is a poet. Levi self-identifies as an Urban Griot (a griot is a traditional consciousness raiser, storyteller, newscaster and political agitator).

Show what you know

1 The poet uses many ways to unveil his identity to the reader. Using the evidence in this poem, what do you know about Levi's appearance?

_____

_____

1

(2 marks)

2 Use the text to explain how we know that Levi's family are important to him.

_____

_____

_____

_____

2

(2 marks)

3 When Levi Tafari performs this poem, he uses rhythm to exaggerate his choice of words. Look at the first verse and comment on how the poet's word-choice creates rhythm.

_____

_____

_____

3

(2 marks)

4 'My identity is a mystery, because my story is not history.' Read this line of the poem and explain how the poet plays with the word 'history' to provide two meanings.

_____

_____

_____

4

(2 marks)

5 Levi's religion influences who he is and his identity. Explain how you know this by referring to the text to support your answer.

_____

_____

_____

_____

5

(3 marks)

/ 11

TOTAL MARKS

Cultural and spiritual influences

Read this extract from *A Suitable Boy* by Vikram Seth, then answer the question below.

A Suitable Boy

In a while they reached Salimpur. They had agreed to meet the others at a cloth and general merchandise shop. But the narrow, crowded streets of Salimpur were completely packed. It was the day of the weekly market. Hawkers, peddlers, vendors of every kind, snake-charmers with their torpid cobras, quacks, tinkers, fruit-sellers with baskets of mangoes and lichis on their heads, sweetsellers, their barfis and laddus and jalebis encrusted with flies, and a great part of the population not only of Salimpur but of many of the surrounding villages, had managed to squeeze into the centre of town.

There was a tremendous din. Above the babble of the customers and the shouts of the hawkers came the conflicting sounds of two screeching loudspeakers, one blaring out the current broadcast from All India Radio Brahmpur, the other interspersing its medley of film songs with advertisements for Raahat-e-Rooh or Ease-for-the-Soul Hair Oil.

Electricity! thought Maan, with a sudden leap of joy. Maybe there'll even be a fan around somewhere.

Netaji, with impatient curses and prolonged beeps of his horn, was hardly able to move a hundred yards in fifteen minutes.

by Vikram Seth

hawker a person who sells goods by shouting
lichis Chinese fruit with a sweet pulp
barfis, laddus, jalebis traditional Indian sweets

Show what you know

1 This extract is taken from a novel set in India. How does the author make the description authentic? Refer to specific words or phrases to support your answer.

(3 marks)

/ 3

Introduction to writing

Your teacher may assess your writing using the following Assessment Foci (AF).

Teacher	Pupil
AF1: Write imaginative, interesting and thoughtful texts	AF1: My writing is imaginative, interesting and thoughtful
AF2: Produce texts which are appropriate to task, reader and purpose	AF2: I am able to write for different purposes and audiences according to the task set
AF3: Organise and present whole texts effectively, sequencing and structuring information, ideas and events	AF3: I can plan my writing and produce texts that sequence ideas, information and events within an appropriate structure
AF4: Construct paragraphs and use cohesion within and between paragraphs	AF4: I can use topic sentences and linking sentences to guide my reader through the text
AF5: Vary sentences for clarity, purpose and effect	AF5: I can use different types of sentences – simple, compound and complex – according to purpose and to create specific effects
AF6: Write with technical accuracy of syntax and punctuation in phrases, clauses and sentences	AF6: I am able to use different types of punctuation to make meaning clear to my reader
AF7: Select appropriate and effective vocabulary	AF7: I can select and use a range of vocabulary, making choices according to purpose and audience
AF8: Use correct spelling	AF8: I can spell accurately

Assessment Foci can be grouped into three strands:

Sentence structure and punctuation	Text structure and organisation	Appropriacy and vocabulary
AF 5 and 6	AF 3 and 4	AF 1 and 2
• Variety of sentence type and length • Range of verb forms used and shifts are managed well • Secure range of appropriate punctuation used for clarity	• Coherence: structure is controlled and suited to the purpose • Cohesion: sections / paragraphs are linked to signal direction clearly for the reader. Ideas are well organised within sections / paragraphs and cohesive devices support purpose	• Writing is adapted addressing the target audience and is focused on the purpose, containing features of the chosen form • Vocabulary choices are ambitious, precise, appropriate and purposeful

Informal and formal language

Answer the following questions on informal and formal language.

Show what you know

1 Read this prompt and identify the purpose, audience, form and formality below.

> At a recent Neighbourhood Watch meeting, it was brought to your attention that the local community are not satisfied with some council issues, for example the unreliability of refuse bin collections, teenagers loitering in the park and limited buses for the elderly. As secretary for the Neighbourhood Watch, you need to report these issues to the council as soon as possible.

Purpose: _____

Audience: _____

Form: _____

Formality: _____

1

(4 marks)

2 In your work, you need to think about *whom* you are writing for and *what* you are writing for. You need to adapt your vocabulary so that it matches your audience and purpose.

Imagine that you are writing the text for two adverts of a new mobile phone: one advert is aimed at teenagers and the other at adults. What **persuasive language** and **phrases** could you use?

a) Advert for teenagers	b) Advert for adults

2a)

(3 marks)

2b)

(3 marks)

/ 10

TOTAL MARKS

Imaginative vocabulary and language

Answer the following questions on imaginative vocabulary.

Show what you know

1 Complete the table with examples of synonyms and antonyms.

Word	Synonym	Antonym
a) bad		
b) light		
c) slow		
d) cold		
e) ugly		
f) quiet		
g) happy		
h) big		
i) sad		
j) loud		

1

(20 marks)

2 Underline the word which means the same as the bold word.

etiquette	pretty	manners	armistice	corsage
defeat	ample	portray	vanquish	surpass
fabulous	hurl	anxious	remarkable	redeem
squander	deploy	attack	waste	volatile
envious	unique	wealthy	jealous	modest
dignified	ambitious	disheartened	noble	captivating
sufficient	weary	enough	majority	expect
awful	compromise	budget	atrocious	precise

2

(8 marks)

/ 28

TOTAL MARKS

37

Parts of speech

Answer the following questions on different parts of speech.

Show what you know

1 Add **pronouns** and **determiners** to this text.

Louisa was _____ amazing mum to _____ three lucky children (Hope, Bill and Poppy). Hope, _____ energetic soon-to-be teenager, excelled at almost everything in _____ school life. Bill was nine and _____ could entertain everybody from close friends to _____ family. As for Poppy, _____ was the personification of cuteness, making everyone smile with _____ infectious giggle.

1

(8 marks)

2 List three **intensifying adverbs** to make this point more strongly.

Warning: Doors close _____ quickly before tram departs.

2

(3 marks)

_____   _____   _____

3 Write a **question tag** in the gaps in these sentences, e.g.:

It's a nice day, **isn't it**?

a) You have booked the train tickets, _____?

b) You do agree that we are spending too much money on our phone bills at the moment, _____?

c) You used to live in Barcelona when you were younger, _____?

d) We will have to order another part for the TV now, _____?

e) This is the same picture you have in your lounge, _____?

3

(5 marks)

4 Correct the two texts below to make them Standard English.

a) My brother and me love dipping biscuits into ours hot chocolate. We do them every day. He sometimes ates his after I go school.

_____

_____

_____

_____

4

(8 marks)

b) 'You don't know nothing about football,' shouted the boy. 'I don't even know why you, like, even come here.'

_____

_____

_____

_____

5 On the lines below, complete the sentences with different **modal verbs**, e.g.:

The rabbits _____ dig a burrow in the summer time.

The rabbits will dig a burrow in the summer time.

a) He _____ _____ gone to his violin lesson, but he forgot.

5

(4 marks)

b) You _____ need your coat as it is raining now!

c) She _____ need some help with her homework.

/ 28

TOTAL MARKS

39

Nouns

We use nouns all the time in sentences. Look at the following example.

Next Tuesday my football team will play in the tournament with pride.

Tuesday	team	tournament
↓	↓	↓
proper noun	collective noun	common noun

Show what you know

1 Identify the nouns in this sentence.

The boy was filled with fear as he realised the gang had caught up with him near Fisher Drive.

_____

_____

1

(4 marks)

2 Identify which type of noun the following words are and label them as proper, common, collective and abstract nouns.

Monday	
table	
mouse	
fleet	
fear	

shoal	
love	
New York	
family	
remorse	

2

(10 marks)

3 Complete this passage with the appropriate nouns from the box.

fire	love	Winter	family	happiness	angels

_____ is my favourite time of year – although it is cold

we can do many _____ activities such as making snowmen,

having snowball fights and creating snow _____. Even

though we need to wear extra layers our hearts are warmed with

_____ and _____ as we drink hot chocolate next to

the _____.

3

(6 marks)

/ 20

TOTAL MARKS

40

Connectives and cohesion

Answer the following questions on connectives and cohesion.

Show what you know

1 Write down four words which mean the same as 'however'.

a) _____ b) _____

c) _____ d) _____

	1
	(4 marks)

2 Write words in the gaps to complete the following sentences.

a) Although _____,

   Miss Barnes _____.

b) After _____,

   the dog _____.

c) Despite _____,

   the nurse _____.

d) Whenever _____,

   my mum _____.

	2
	(8 marks)

3 When writing persuasively, you can use different words and phrases to structure your writing and to help cohesion.

Match the examples below on the left to their functions on the right by drawing lines to connect them.

to link paragraphs and to show addition	to sum up, in conclusion
to give examples	similarly
to compare	however, on the other hand
to contrast	for instance
to conclude	furthermore

	3
	(5 marks)

	/ 17

TOTAL MARKS

Identifying phrases

Answer the following questions on identifying phrases.

Show what you know

1 Fill in the table below using phrases from this sentence.

A Labrador puppy needs to be at least six months old before it can be separated from its mother.

Noun phrase	
Verb phrase	
Prepositional phrase	
Adjectival phrase	

☐ 1
(4 marks)

2 Add three prepositional phrases to the following sentences to provide more detail for the reader.

Think about who, what and how.

a) The girls read and talked.

_____

_____

_____

☐ 2
(6 marks)

b) The boys ran and cheered.

_____

_____

_____

3 Write three different subject noun phrases to complete this sentence.

a) _____ played in the rounders match.

b) _____ played in the rounders match.

c) _____ played in the rounders match.

☐ 3
(3 marks)

☐ / 13

TOTAL MARKS

42

Identifying independent and dependent clauses

Answer the following questions to show how to identify independent and dependent clauses.

Show what you know

1 Complete the table by ticking the correct clause.

	Independent clause	Dependent clause	Phrase
although it was 9 p.m.			
the bell rang			
whenever he had time			
unless it was hot			
the cat ran			
during the night			
a small, green insect			
smiling sweetly and innocently			
even though she was sick			

1

(9 marks)

2 Insert a phrase with at least four words in it on each line.

a) The _____ ran through the forest.

b) Opening the door, _____ climbed the stairs.

c) Looking around, _____ noticed the old boat.

2

(3 marks)

3 Underline the independent clause in each sentence and add any necessary punctuation.

a) Freddie who usually loved rice threw his dinner on the floor.

b) Even though Pritika was the youngest she won the race.

c) The sun shone all day so we all got burnt.

3

(3 marks)

/ 15

TOTAL MARKS

43

Identifying main and subordinate clauses

This sentence is made up of two clauses, a main clause and a subordinate clause.

Imran's Uncle Frank, who loves travelling, always stays in hotels.

Answer the following questions to show how to identify main and subordinate clauses.

Show what you know

1 Add a subordinate clause to each of the sentences below.

   a) We ran, _____
   _____ , to school.

   b) She screamed, _____
   _____ , at the dog.

   c) My next door neighbour Sarah, _____
   _____ , is a doctor.

   d) Sarah's niece Eva, _____
   _____ , enjoys watching football.

   e) Dermot's brother, _____
   _____ , lives in Ireland.

2 Underline the subordinate clause in each sentence.

   a) After Pritika smashed the vase, she tried to fix it with glue.

   b) While Imran waited for his train, he checked his emails and ate a sandwich.

   c) Samuel completed all of his homework, since he had been in trouble at school.

Tenses

Answer the following questions on simple present, simple past and simple future tenses.

Show what you know

1 Complete this verb tense grid, giving appropriate versions of the sentences.

Simple present	Simple past	Simple future
I eat a banana every day.	Yesterday I ate a banana.	Tomorrow I am going to eat a banana.
Present continuous	Past continuous	Future continuous
a)	b)	c)
Present perfect	Past perfect	Future perfect
d)	e)	f)
Present perfect continuous	Past perfect continuous	Future perfect continuous
g)	h)	i)

1

(9 marks)

2 Use the words in parentheses to complete these sentences with the correct tenses.

a) You look really great! Have (you, work out) _____ at the gym recently?

b) What (you do) _____ when the fire alarm went off?

c) I (have) _____ the same car for six years.

d) Wendy (arrive) _____ in Newcastle at 6 p.m.

e) People who work in libraries are (call) _____ librarians.

f) If she (keep) _____ arriving late, she (eventually, lose) _____ her job.

g) Hopefully when we (wake) _____ up tomorrow morning, the sun (shine) _____ .

h) If you (need) _____ me next Friday, I (stay) _____ at my mum's house.

2

(8 marks)

/ 17

TOTAL MARKS

Modal verbs

Answer the following questions on modal verbs.

Show what you know

1 Choose the correct modal verb to complete each sentence below.

a) The boys _____ gone to see the head teacher.

must be	must do	must have

1

(6 marks)

b) When I lived in Calcutta, we _____ often eat food from street vendors.

might	would	should

c) I don't know where Luke is. He _____ in the lounge or the garden.

might sit	might have sat	might be sitting

d) You _____ the air pressure in your tyres before you leave.

ought to check	ought to be checking	ought to have been checking

e) You can't mean that! You _____ .

must joke	have got to be joking	have to have joked

f) The machine _____ on later by clicking this switch.

can be turning	can have turned	can be turned

/ 6

TOTAL MARKS

Managing shifts in your writing

A shift in verb forms means to change from one tense to another. This sometimes happens when one event takes place before another event.

> At the first Christmas concert the children will sing some carols that they learned during the autumn term.

Show what you know

1 Write the correct verb form(s) to complete these sentences.

a) Suddenly I (saw) _____ a fox in front of my car,

   so I (slam) _____ on my brakes and the car (skid)

   _____ .

b) The baby (knock) _____ the drink off the table,

   so I (go) _____ to make him another drink.

c) When I (finish) _____ writing my letter, I (put)

   _____ it in an envelope.

d) After the cake has (cool) _____ down, I (decorate)

   _____ it with your name.

e) Jackie wants to (show) _____ her friends the

   photos she (take) _____ last summer.

f) Hundreds of children will (see) _____ the

   exhibition by the time it (close) _____ next spring.

1

(13 marks)

/ 13

TOTAL MARKS

47

Subjunctive mood

Your writing has two moods: indicative and subjunctive.

A sentence in the indicative mood is a statement of fact.
A sentence in the subjunctive mood indicates that something is conditional or doubtful.

Indicative

It was ➞ It were

If it were not for you, I would have no money.

Subjunctive

I was ➞ I would

If I were rich, I would buy a blue, sporty car.

Show what you know

1 Complete these subjunctive sentences so that it is clear to the reader that they are written in the subjunctive mood.

a) If you were older, _____ .

b) If it were not for you, _____ .

c) If I were prime minister, _____ .

d) If Kirshanda had known about the test, _____

_____ .

1

(4 marks)

/ 4

TOTAL MARKS

48

Active and passive

Answer the following questions on active and passive voice.

Show what you know

1 Rewrite these sentences, changing them from the active to the passive voice.

Active voice	Passive voice
a) Claire drank a cup of coffee.	
b) Alex ate a doughnut.	
c) The team won a trophy.	
d) Bal cleaned the windows.	
e) Jackie drove the car.	
f) Pete read the newspaper.	

2 Rewrite these sentences, changing them from the passive to the active voice.

Active voice	Passive voice
a)	**a)** The bins were emptied by Dermot.
b)	**b)** An apple pie was baked by Pammy.
c)	**c)** The competition was won by the juggler.
d)	**d)** The mouse was chased by the cat.
e)	**e)** The accounts were calculated by Raj.
f)	**f)** The children were woken by the alarm.

1

(6 marks)

2

(6 marks)

/ 12

TOTAL MARKS

Adverbs and pronouns

Answer the following questions on adverbs and pronouns.

Show what you know

1 Look at this list of adverbs and tick the right column for each one.

Adverb	Manner (how)	Time (when)	Place (where)
today			
hard			
everywhere			
here			
bravely			
weekly			
innocently			
normally			
honestly			
anywhere			

2 Look at this list of pronouns and tick whether each one is a possessive pronoun, personal pronoun or relative pronoun.

Pronoun	Possessive pronoun	Personal pronoun	Relative pronoun
our			
him			
your			
she			
which			
you			

1
(5 marks)

2
(3 marks)

/ 8

TOTAL MARKS

50

Expanded noun phrases

In noun phrases, where the key word is a noun, there are many ways in which the noun can be expanded by adding words in front or after the noun to create an expanded noun phrase.

the car
the car near the church
the blue sports car near the church

Show what you know

1 Write noun phrases by adding some words before and after each noun.

Noun	Expanded noun phrase
house	
pen	
cat	
tree	
chair	

1

(5 marks)

Changing nouns to verbs and changing verbs to nouns

Show what you know

1 Change the nouns in this list to verbs.

Noun	Verb
disruption	
explorer	
success	
preparation	

2 Change the verbs in this list to nouns.

Noun	Verb
	to apologise
	to negotiate
	to standardise
	to synchronise

1

(2 marks)

2

(2 marks)

/ 9

TOTAL MARKS

51

Punctuation and clarity

Answer the following questions on punctuation and clarity.

Show what you know

1 Insert a colon and four commas into the sentence below to clarify its meaning.

> For example, you can fill the basket with the following nappies baby wipes baby lotion baby powder baby oil and bottles.

[ ] 1

(5 marks)

2 Insert a semi-colon into each of the sentences below to clarify the meaning of the sentences.

> **a)** Call me tomorrow I will give you my answer then.

[ ] 2

(3 marks)

> **b)** No one was seriously injured in the fire one girl suffered minor facial burns.

> **c)** Claire always slept with the light on she was afraid of the dark.

3 Rewrite this text as direct speech. Make up a name for the pupil.

> I told Miss Richens that I didn't have my homework because I had left it at home and she said that I had a detention, but then Miss McCoy interrupted and said that my mum had dropped it off for me.

_____

_____

_____

_____

_____

[ ] 3

(3 marks)

[ ] / 11

TOTAL MARKS

Using apostrophes accurately

Answer the following questions on using apostrophes correctly.

Show what you know

1 Look at the use of apostrophes in this list and tick the correct column.

	Apostrophe for omission	Apostrophe for possession
the cat's ball		
the men's cars		
I can't see		
don't do that		
Mum's bag		
we won't do that		
the car's wheel		
that isn't good enough		
the children's coats		
the teachers' desks		
you shouldn't run		
the footballers' boots		

1

(24 marks)

2 Add three apostrophes to this passage.

2

(4 marks)

Many children in the playground were playing with either balls or bats. Year 6 had responsibility for tidying up the sports equipment after the afternoons activities. Suddenly, the wind began to blow and the children couldnt collect the balls. Mrs Morris reminded the girls that it was their turn to collect everybodys coats.

/ 27

TOTAL MARKS

Using brackets and dashes

Brackets are used to give stage directions on how to speak in play-scripts:

> *Faye:* (pointing at watch) You are late. I've been waiting for an hour!

Brackets also allow the writer to speak directly to the reader in an aside:

> She was sitting there behind the door (you know where I mean).

Dashes can be used to indicate a slightly longer pause than a comma. This can build tension, introduce a new idea or indicate comic timing:

- He sprinted across the road, climbed over the wall, crept under the windowsill – safe at last.

- She was walking through the crowds, waving her arms like the Queen – when her trousers split!

Now answer the following question on brackets and dashes.

Show what you know

1 Change the extract below into a play-script using stage directions.

> It was a cold wintry morning and Eleanor rubbed her hands together as she moaned and called to her mum. Mum was cleaning in the kitchen and reminded Eleanor that she had already told her twice to get her hat, scarf and gloves. As Eleanor ran in to do as she was told, she slipped on the ice and called for Mum again. Upon realising that Eleanor was in trouble, Mum ran to the garden and screamed with concern when she saw Eleanor's twisted leg.

1

(4 marks)

/ 4

TOTAL MARKS

Word families

Word families are words that can be grouped in a particular way:

- through a spelling pattern
- meaning
- by the inclusion of a particular root word.

Word families are important because they often reveal hidden patterns in words.

Show what you know

(1) Complete the table below by writing the nouns and adjectives next to the verb in each word family.

Example	Noun	Adjective	Past participle
accept			
achieve			
admire			
bore			
confide			
confuse			
disappoint			
lie (not tell the truth)			
punish			
murder			
amaze			
appreciate			
educate			
impress			
progress			

/ 15

TOTAL MARKS

Etymology

Answer the following question on etymology.

Show what you know

1 Use a dictionary to find the definition, origin and word class for the following words.

Word	Definition	Origin	Word class
a) scrutinise			
b) obliterate			
c) liaise			
d) cantankerous			

1
(12 marks)

Prefixes and suffixes

If you know prefixes and suffixes and their meanings it will help you to build multi-syllabic words, especially where sounds change.

Show what you know

1 Write four examples for each suffix.

-ist	-ous	-ster	-tion	-sion	-ise
pianist					

/ 12
TOTAL MARKS

1
(24 marks)

2 Write four examples for each prefix.

inter-	il-	semi-	trans-	co-	post-
interface					

2
(24 marks)

/ 48
TOTAL MARKS

Homographs

Homographs (from the Greek words **homos**, meaning 'the same' and **graphein**, meaning 'to write') are words that are spelled the same, but have different meanings and often different pronunciation, for example:

> bow (bow and arrow)
> bow (bow down)

Show what you know

1 Write a sentence using each of these homographs correctly.

a) minute	b) minute	c) row	d) row
e) wound	f) wound	g) sewer	h) sewer
i) dear	j) dear	k) wind	l) wind

a) _____

b) _____

c) _____

d) _____

e) _____

f) _____

g) _____

h) _____

i) _____

j) _____

k) _____

l) _____

1

(12 marks)

/ 12

TOTAL MARKS

57

Homophones

Homophones (from the Greek words **homos**, meaning 'the same' and **phone**, meaning 'sound') are words which are **pronounced the same**, but which have **different spellings and meanings**, for example:

> feet / feat
> knight / night

Now answer the following question on homophones.

Show what you know

1 Some homophones are confusing. Write a definition for each of these homophones.

a) complement _____

b) compliment _____

c) discreet _____

d) discrete _____

e) lead _____

f) led _____

g) hare _____

h) hair _____

i) loose _____

j) lose _____

k) plane _____

l) plain _____

m) practice _____

n) practise _____

o) warn _____

p) worn _____

1

(16 marks)

/ 16

TOTAL MARKS

Identifying syllables

As words become more complex, they don't always follow a simple spelling rule. Instead, you may find it helpful to visualise how the different syllables are spelled and then put the word back together, for example:

> horrible = hor + ri + ble

You will need to use your knowledge of suffixes when identifying the syllables tion, cian, ble.

Now answer the following question on identifying syllables.

Show what you know

1 Break the following words into their syllable blocks.

persevere	
influence	
demonstrate	
accommodate	
excavate	
correspond	
appreciate	
exaggerate	
atmosphere	
mosquito	
pronunciation	
terminate	
ventilate	
guarantee	
magician	

1

(15 marks)

/ 15

TOTAL MARKS

Writing prompt

As part of the Level 6 writing test you may be required to complete an unseen writing task. Read the prompt below and allow yourself 30 minutes to respond to the task. If necessary, use another piece of paper to finish your writing.

> Your school is advertising for a new head teacher and the local council is keen to give candidates a pupil's perspective of the school. They are requesting a written account which they intend to use during the interview process. The content of the account has not been prescribed. However, whatever you write will represent the pupil voice from your school.

Tips

- Use a variety of sentence types. Think about which style of writing would best suit this task.

- Write a well-organised account supported by the accurate use of punctuation.

- Choose imaginative and appropriate vocabulary to convey meaning.